JUDGE REG AND THE GRUDGE BROTHERS

Clive Gifford

Illustrated by Elisa Squillace

The town of Lamb Ridge welcomed their new judge, Reg. Some said he was the toughest lawman in the **Wild West**.

Others had heard he had fought in foreign campaigns and wars. He asked for fudge as his reward when he caught outlaws.

Lamb Ridge needed a tough judge, all its people believed. The town was under attack from a family of thieves. The Grudge Brothers stole everything from money to lambs.

Smudge Grudge was the eldest and, my, was he tough.
Nudge Grudge was younger but still rather rough.
The Grudges robbed the general store, stealing flour and hams.
Even their little sister, Madge, stole babies' prams!

GENERAL STORE

Some words have letters that you can't hear when the word is spoken. Say each word and look to see which letter is 'silent', then circle it.

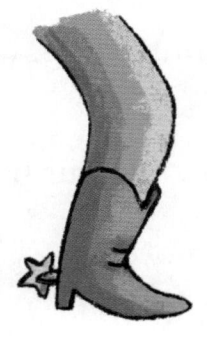

limb

debt

design

reign

subtle

doubt

gnome

gnarled

campaign

combed

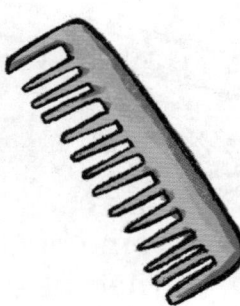

3

Judge Reg combed his hair and tried to look his best.
He proudly received his judge's badge and pinned it to his chest.

He made a speech, standing on the ledge
outside his Judge's Lodge.

WELCOME
JUDGE
REG

"I, Judge Reg, and my faithful horse,
Midge, make a pledge:
to make Lamb Ridge safe,
so you can all sleep soundly in your beds.
We will comb the creeks,
plains and fields, and will not rest
until we've put the Grudges in jail,
so they can no longer be pests."

WANTED

4

The cheering of the crowd wasn't as loud as it ought to have been.
Some of Lamb Ridge were disappointed at what they had seen.
Their new judge was tiny. He couldn't be any smaller!
And to be a good judge, should Reg not be taller?

WANTED

Can you work out which of these eight words can have re added to them?

____ sort

____ main

____ lease

____ please

____ sense

____ heat

____ store

____ less

____ port

____ view

____ vent

____ quest

"**Y**ou're no taller than a garden gnome," cried a voice that rasped. The voice was Madge Grudge's. The crowd turned and gasped.

"You're no match for my rough, tough brothers," said Madge. "They'll run you out of town, just like they did to other judges."

Madge picked up a ball of mud outside the Judge's Lodge.

"Take that, you little gnat!" said Madge, as she flicked the mud. The mud missed Reg's head, but hit his new judge's badge.

"You will regret doing that, Madge Grudge," said Judge Reg.

In a flash, he handcuffed her and locked her in a cell in the Lodge.

"I may be small, but I react faster than anyone in the Wild West." The people of Lamb Ridge looked on. Most were impressed.

Some of the letters have been shot out of these signs in Lamb Ridge by the Grudge Brothers. Fill the gaps with the missing letters to complete the words.

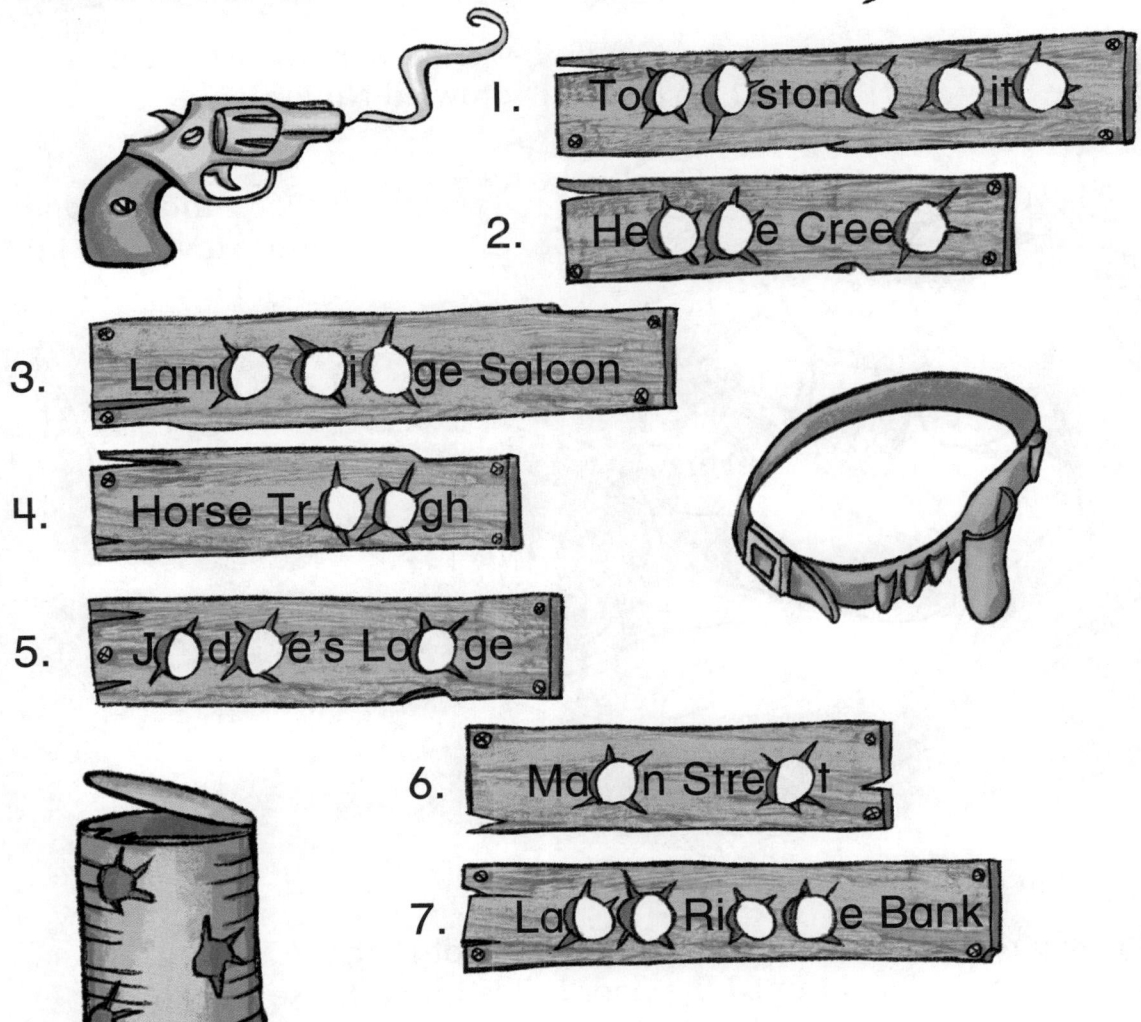

1. To⬤ ⬤ston⬤ ⬤it⬤

2. He⬤⬤e Cree⬤

3. Lam⬤ ⬤i⬤ge Saloon

4. Horse Tr⬤⬤gh

5. J⬤d⬤e's Lo⬤ge

6. Ma⬤n Stre⬤t

7. La⬤⬤Ri⬤⬤e Bank

Judge Reg walked through Lamb Ridge, eating some fudge.
He had just read about the legend of a monster made out of sludge.
The monster was said to live in a place nearby called Hedge Creek.
As Reg thought about it, he heard hooves and then someone speak.

"We hear you locked our sister up, Judge," snarled Smudge.

"You'd better let her go, or there'll be trouble," growled Nudge.

"I regret that Madge will be staying in jail for a while," said Reg.

Smudge said,
"Let her go, you dumb gnome, or we'll get **tough**."

Judge Reg refused and the Grudge Brothers got rough.
Nudge and Smudge dumped the poor Judge into a horse trough.
They both cackled and scoffed before they rode off.

Here is part of the legend of the sludge monster which Judge Reg read. Can you underline all the words which are verbs and circle all the words which are adjectives?

A long time ago, the creek was a mighty river and not the sludgy stream it is today. The first time the creek ran dry, a strange thing occurred. From the thick mud and stinking sludge at the bottom of the rushing creek, something stirred. A giant creature called the sludge monster rose up. It strode across the land and scared any creature that it found. The scary monster has gone, but one day it may rise from the sludgy stream again.

9

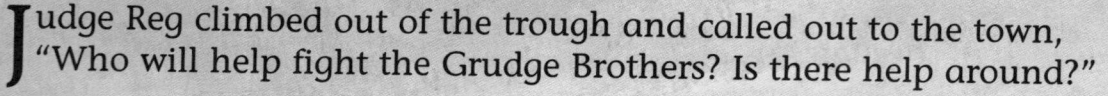

Judge Reg climbed out of the trough and called out to the town,
"Who will help fight the Grudge Brothers? Is there help around?"

The people of Lamb Ridge looked down. No one made a sound.

"Just you and me, Midge," said Reg. "What a shame, what a pity.
Time to ride past Hedge Creek to get help from Tombstone City."

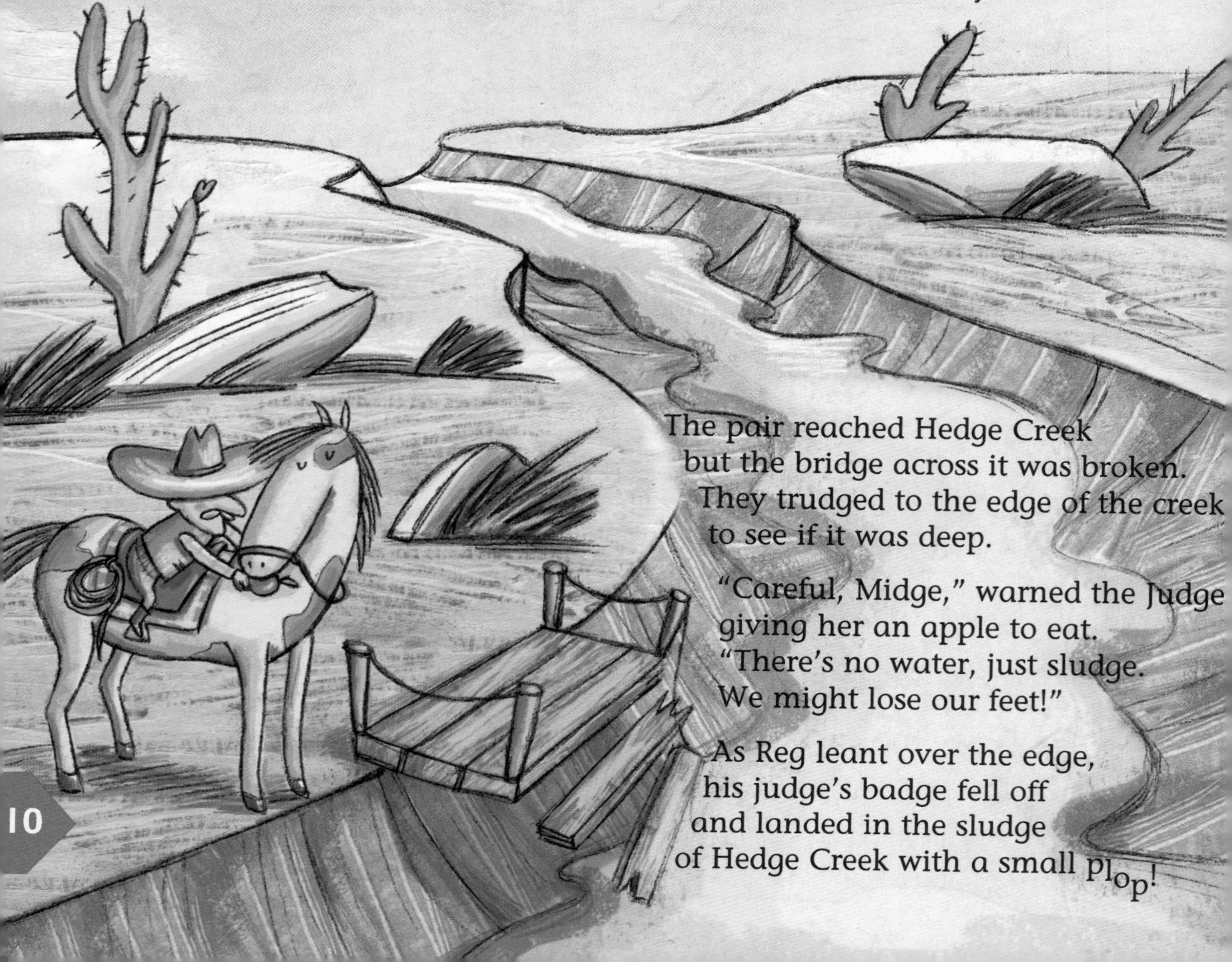

The pair reached Hedge Creek
but the bridge across it was broken.
They trudged to the edge of the creek
to see if it was deep.

"Careful, Midge," warned the Judge
giving her an apple to eat.
"There's no water, just sludge.
We might lose our feet!"

As Reg leant over the edge,
his judge's badge fell off
and landed in the sludge
of Hedge Creek with a small plop!

Read the descriptions of the Grudge family and then write the correct name above each adjective.

Smudge Grudge is not as heavy as Nudge, but is not as light as Madge. He is smarter and meaner than both of them.

Nudge Grudge is meaner than Madge, but is not as loud as Madge or Smudge.

Madge Grudge is louder, smarter and lighter than Nudge and lighter and louder than Smudge.

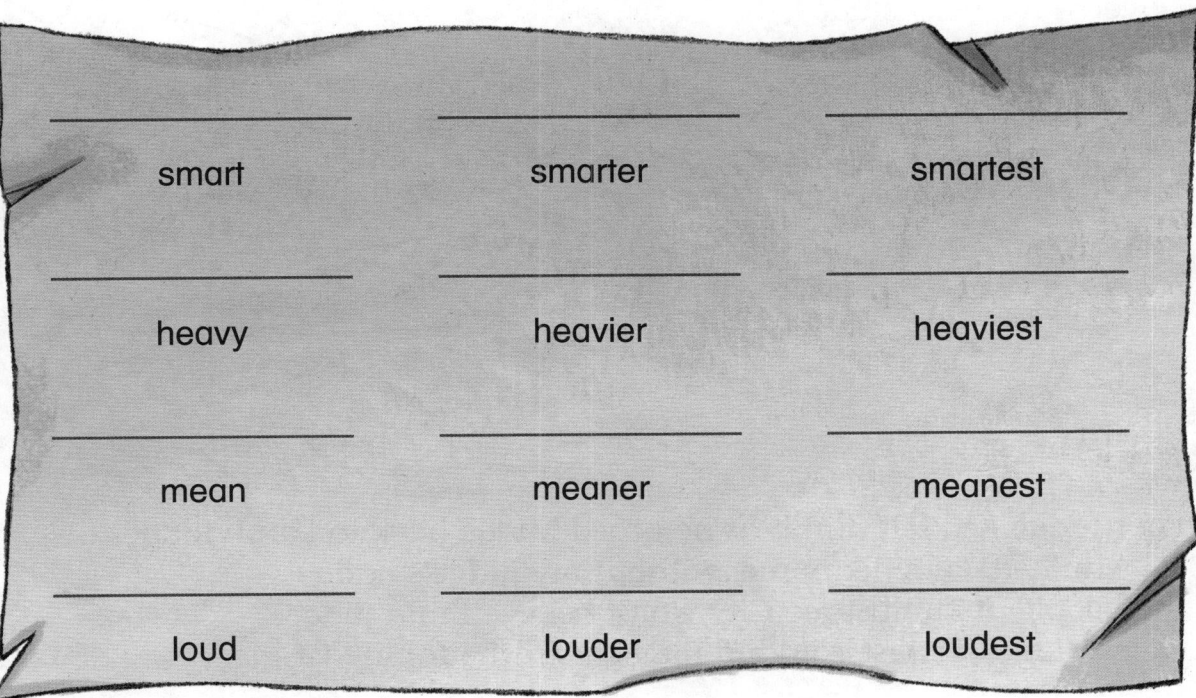

smart	smarter	smartest
heavy	heavier	heaviest
mean	meaner	meanest
loud	louder	loudest

"Oh crumbs, I'm dumb!" cursed Judge Reg.
"This isn't great timing."

He and Midge looked down
and thought they saw the badge shining.
But they leant too far over the edge
and, with a **SPLOSH**, both fell in!

Judge Reg and Midge dredged the sludge of Hedge Creek.
But no matter how hard they searched,
they couldn't find the badge.

Then they climbed out of Hedge
Creek, covered in sticky sludge.
The sun baked the sludge on so hard,
it just wouldn't budge.

Poor Judge Reg felt numb as he urged Midge back to Lamb Ridge.
He whinged, "Oh deary me, without my judge's badge
the people of Tombstone City won't believe I'm a judge.
Dear Midge, it's just you and me against the family Grudge!"

There are ten words hidden in the grid. See if you can find them all and use the clues to help.

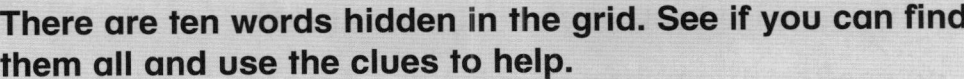

1. To sketch something before it is made.

2. A structure which crosses a valley or river.

3. An object worn by sheriffs.

4. To smear.

5. To fake or pretend something.

6. A garden ornament.

7. To take a vow or make a promise.

8. To not feel anything.

9. A small insect beginning with the letter **g**.

10. Not able to speak, also used to mean stupid.

T	B	R	I	D	G	E
A	M	C	O	E	N	P
N	U	M	B	S	O	L
G	D	Y	A	I	M	E
S	M	U	D	G	E	D
F	E	I	G	N	R	G
G	S	T	E	R	H	E

Judge Reg and Midge turned into Main Street, back in Lamb Ridge.
Right there stood the Grudge Brothers, on a ledge outside the Judge's Lodge.

They were up to no good, trying to break their sister out of jail.

Nudge Grudge looked over
at Judge Reg and began to turn pale.

Judge Reg was puzzled
by the reaction of Nudge Grudge.
Last time he had seen the Judge,
Nudge had laughed and scoffed.
Now, he was trembling
and looked like he was in shock.

Judge Reg took a look at his reflection
in the window of a store.
He and Midge were still covered in sludge,
from their heads to the floor.
He remembered the legend
of the sludge monster of Hedge Creek.
He thought up a cunning plan,
then he started to speak.

Can you draw lines between the columns to create new words?

rest   lace

plum   ill

re   range

led   ore

rep   bing

bo   ge

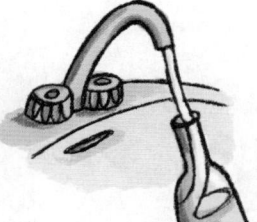

ref   do

rear   rough

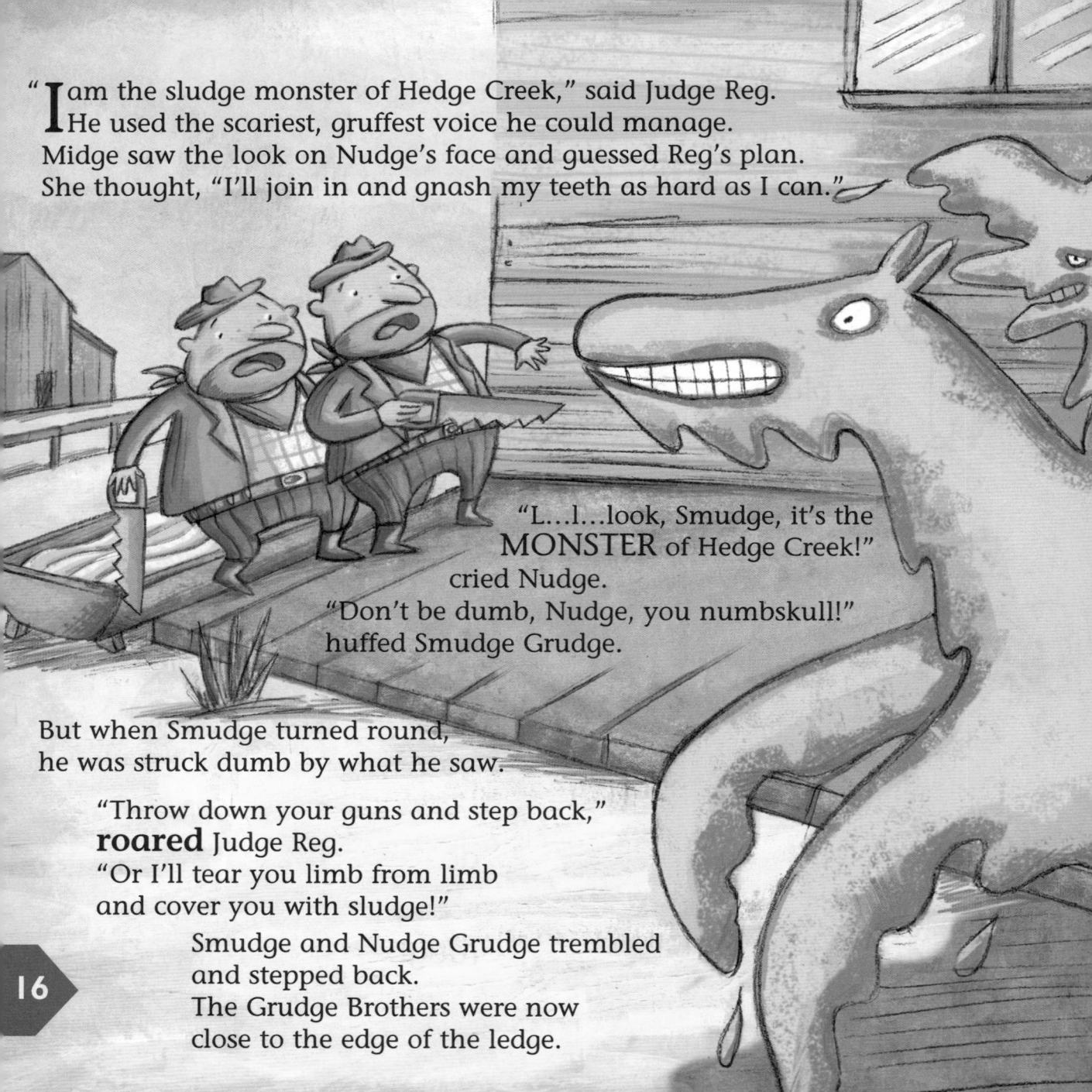

"I am the sludge monster of Hedge Creek," said Judge Reg.
He used the scariest, gruffest voice he could manage.
Midge saw the look on Nudge's face and guessed Reg's plan.
She thought, "I'll join in and gnash my teeth as hard as I can."

"L...l...look, Smudge, it's the
MONSTER of Hedge Creek!"
cried Nudge.
"Don't be dumb, Nudge, you numbskull!"
huffed Smudge Grudge.

But when Smudge turned round,
he was struck dumb by what he saw.

"Throw down your guns and step back,"
roared Judge Reg.
"Or I'll tear you limb from limb
and cover you with sludge!"

Smudge and Nudge Grudge trembled
and stepped back.
The Grudge Brothers were now
close to the edge of the ledge.

16

Can you create a "Wanted" poster similar to the one for Smudge Grudge, but about a friend or relative? Make up two funny crimes that they are wanted for and fill in their description, using lots of detail.

WANTED

Jimmy 'Smudge' Grudge

For:
lamb rustling
and bank robbing.

Description: Smudge Grudge has black hair and brown eyes. He is six feet tall and wears a large Stetson hat. Do not approach this man – he is dangerous!

WANTED

For: _____

and _____

Description: _____

_____

_____

_____

_____

_____

_____

_____

_____

_____

_____

"Step back, again," roared Reg, as Midge gnashed her teeth. The Grudges stepped over the edge of the ledge and, just as Reg hoped, they fell into the horse trough. **SPLOSH!**

Quick as a flash, Judge Reg jumped off Midge's back. He whipped out his handcuffs. The Grudge Brothers were trapped!

Judge Reg locked the Grudge Brothers inside the Judge's Lodge. He said, "I'm sure you'll be pleased to join your little sister, Madge."

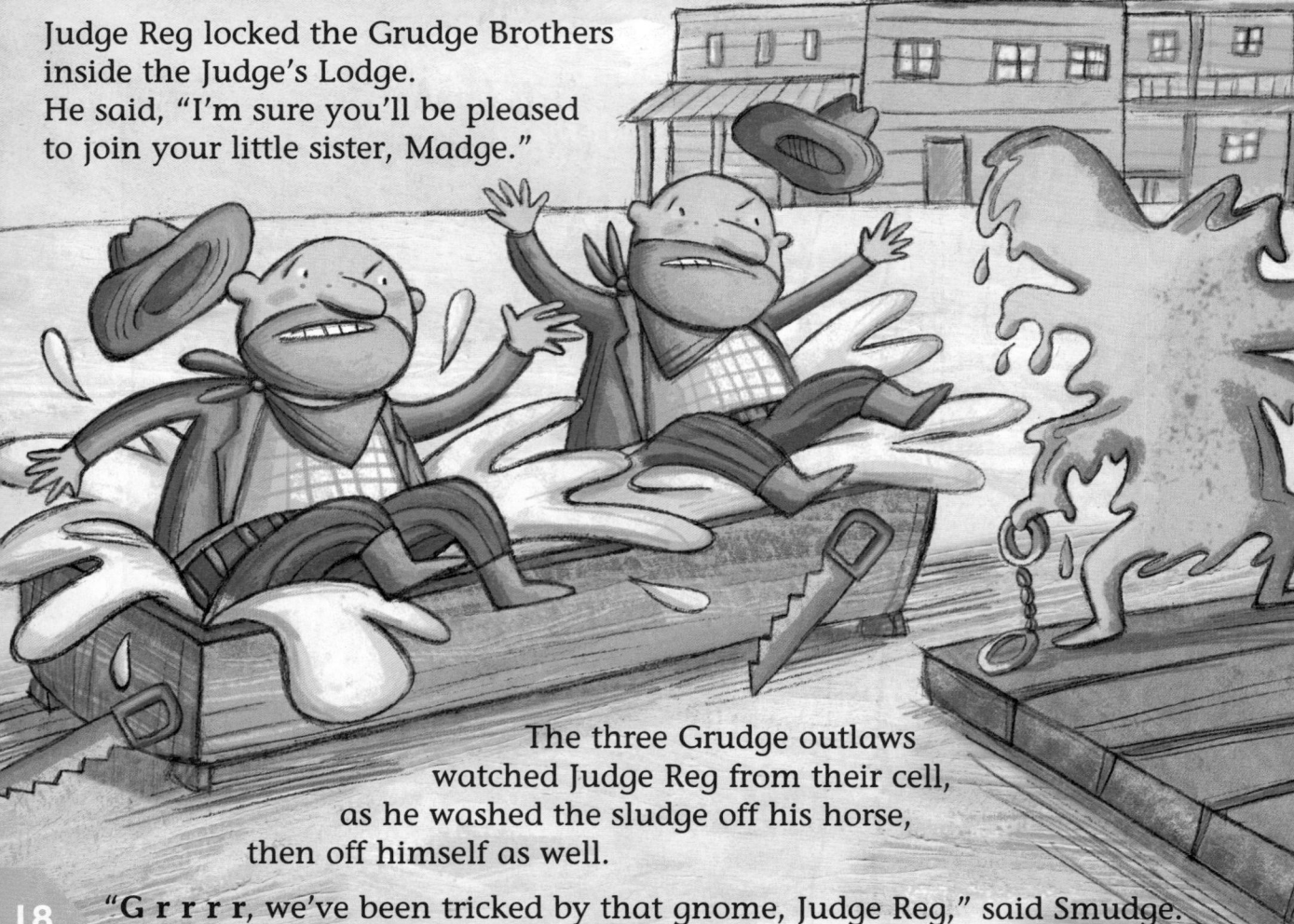

The three Grudge outlaws watched Judge Reg from their cell, as he washed the sludge off his horse, then off himself as well.

"**G r r r r**, we've been tricked by that gnome, Judge Reg," said Smudge.

"I can't believe that little gnat has beaten us," wailed Nudge.

Add a letter to the front of each set of letters to make new words. Write the new words out in full.

reek _____

mudge _____

limb _____

rumb _____

ridge _____ _____

edge _____ _____ _____

ought _____ _____ _____ _____

ough _____ _____ _____

_____ _____

19

The people of Lamb Ridge cheered
and sighed with relief.
Judge Reg and Midge had saved
their town from the thieves.
But some people hung their
heads in shame.
Why hadn't they helped
the Judge in his campaign?
They feared that he might
now decide to retire or resign.

Lamb Ridge pledged to reward their small, but tough judge.
First, they gave him a lifetime's supply of free fudge.

Then, they built a bigger Judge's Lodge, with a stable for Midge.
And Reg was given a new, larger, shinier judge's badge.

20

Midge got her own badge too, and lots and lots of fresh hay.
And for years, Judge Reg and Midge happily kept trouble at bay.

Can you answer these questions about the story of Judge Reg and the Grudge Brothers?

 1. What was the name of the town where Reg became Judge? _____

 2. What did Madge Grudge steal? _____

3. What was the name of the oldest Grudge Brother? _____

 4. Who threw mud at Judge Reg? _____

 5. What was the Judge's horse called? _____

 6. Who was the first character in the story to end up in the horse trough? _____

 7. Can you name the place Judge Reg and his horse were going to visit for help? _____

 8. What was the name of the place where Judge Reg lost his badge? _____

 9. What did Judge Reg receive a free supply of for life? _____

21

Answers

Page 3

lim**b**　　desi**gn**
de**b**t　　su**b**tle
rei**gn**　　**gn**ome
dou**b**t　　campai**gn**
gnarled　　com**b**ed

Page 5

resort　　release
remain　　restore
reheat　　report
review　　request

Page 7

1. Tombstone City
2. Hedge Creek
3. Lamb Ridge Saloon
4. Horse Trough
5. Judge's Lodge
6. Main Street
7. Lamb Ridge Bank

Page 9

A (long) time ago, the creek <u>was</u> a (mighty) river and not the (sludgy) stream it <u>is</u> today. The (first) time the creek <u>ran</u> (dry), a (strange) thing <u>occurred</u>. From the (thick) mud and (stinking) sludge at the bottom of the (rushing) creek, something <u>stirred</u>. A (giant) creature <u>called</u> the sludge monster <u>rose</u> up. It <u>strode</u> across the land and <u>scared</u> any creature that it <u>found</u>. The (scary) monster <u>has gone</u>, but one day it <u>may</u> <u>rise</u> from the (sludgy) stream again.

Page 11

Nudge	Madge	Smudge
smart	**smarter**	**smartest**
Madge	Smudge	Nudge
heavy	**heavier**	**heaviest**
Madge	Nudge	Smudge
mean	**meaner**	**meanest**
Nudge	Smudge	Madge
loud	**louder**	**loudest**

Page 13

1. design
2. bridge
3. badge
4. smudge
5. feign
6. gnome
7. pledge
8. numb
9. gnat
10. dumb

T	B	R	I	D	G	E
A	M	C	O	E	N	P
N	U	M	B	S	O	L
G	D	Y	A	I	M	E
S	M	U	D	G	E	D
F	E	I	G	N	R	G
G	S	T	E	R	H	E

Page 15

rest ore → restore
plum bing → plumbing
re do → redo
led ge → ledge
rep lace → replace
bo rough → borough
ref ill → refill
rear range → rearrange

Page 17

Check your child's work for spelling,
grammar and punctuation.

Page 19

reek → creek
mudge → smudge
limb → climb
rumb → crumb
ridge → bridge fridge
edge → hedge ledge wedge
ought → bought fought
        nought sought
ough → bough cough dough
        rough tough

Page 21

1. Lamb Ridge
2. babies' prams
3. Smudge Grudge
4. Madge Grudge
5. Midge
6. Judge Reg
7. Tombstone City
8. Hedge Creek
9. fudge

Published 2005

Letts Educational, The Chiswick Centre,
414 Chiswick High Road, London W4 5TF
Tel 020 8996 3333   Fax 020 8996 8390
Email mail@lettsed.co.uk
www.letts-education.com

Text, design and illustrations © Letts Educational Ltd 2005
Nelson handwriting font © Thomas Nelson

Book Concept, Development and Series Editor:
Helen Jacobs, Publishing Director
Author: Clive Gifford
Book Design: 2idesign Ltd, Cambridge
Illustrations: Elisa Squillace, The Bright Agency

British Library Cataloguing in Publication Data

A CIP record for this book is available from the British Library.

ISBN 978-1-84315-491-4

Printed in Italy

Colour reproduction by PDQ Digital Media Solutions Ltd, Bungay,
Suffolk NR35 1BY